An Nasihah

Islamic Curriculum

المنهج الاسلامي للأطفال

Workbook 2

Fiqh   `Aqā'id

Aḥādīth   Akhlāq

Sīrah   Ādāb

Tārīkh   Islam

Learning Time!

An Nasihah Publications

Every effort has been made to ensure the correctness of the content. The publishers will gladly receive information enabling them to rectify any error or omission in subsequent editions.

First Edition March 2016
Second Edition July 2016

An Nasihah Publications Ltd.
114 Harborough Road
Leicester LE2 4LD
United Kingdom

www.an-nasihah.com
admin@an-nasihah.com

Distributors in the UK: Azhar Academy, London
www.azharacademy.com

British Library Cataloguing in Publication Data
A catalogue record for this book is available from the British Library.

Name: _____

Class: _____

اَلْحَمْدُ لِلّٰهِ رَبِّ الْعَالَمِيْنَ
وَالصَّلَاةُ وَالسَّلَامُ عَلَى نَبِيِّنَا مُحَمَّدٍ
وَعَلَى اٰلِهِ وَصَحْبِهِ أَجْمَعِيْنَ

بِسْمِ اللّٰهِ الرَّحْمٰنِ الرَّحِيْمِ

Contents

Fiqh

Keeping Clean

Colour in and learn the key words:

Ṭahārah

Istinjā'

Wuḍū'

Ghusl

Keywords

Place each word from the boxes below next to the correct definition.

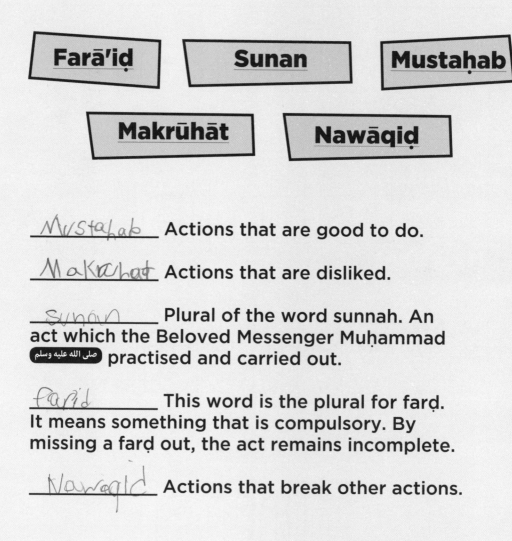

Farā'iḍ

Sunan

Mustaḥab

Makrūhāt

Nawāqiḍ

Mustahab Actions that are good to do.

Makruhat Actions that are disliked.

Sunan Plural of the word sunnah. An act which the Beloved Messenger Muḥammad  practised and carried out.

Farid This word is the plural for farḍ. It means something that is compulsory. By missing a farḍ out, the act remains incomplete.

Nawaqid Actions that break other actions.

How many of each in wuḍū'?

Help Sājid connect the words in wuḍū' to the correct number:

The first one has been done for you.

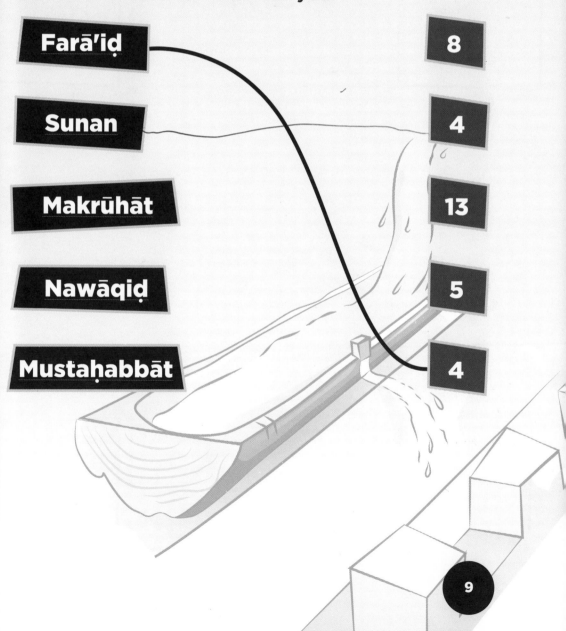

Farā'iḍ

Sunan

Makrūhāt

Nawāqiḍ

Mustaḥabbāt

8

4

13

5

4

Farā'iḍ of Wuḍū'

Colour the number four and write the four farā'iḍ of wuḍū' around the number.

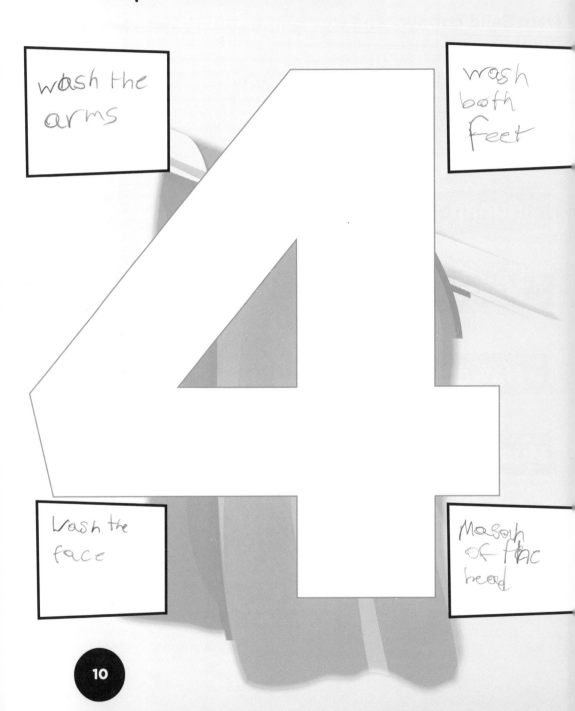

wash the arms

wash both feet

Wash the face

Masah of the head

Farā'iḍ of Wuḍū'

Put the following four boxes in order by placing the correct number under them.

Colour the writing in once you've put them in order.

Wash the arms

Number: 3

Wash both feet

Number: 4

Wash the face

Number: 1

Masaḥ of the head

Number: 2

Sunan of Wuḍū'

Yūsuf wants to use the miswāk during wuḍū' which is a sunnah of wuḍū'. Help Yūsuf reach his miswāk so he can practice upon this sunnah.

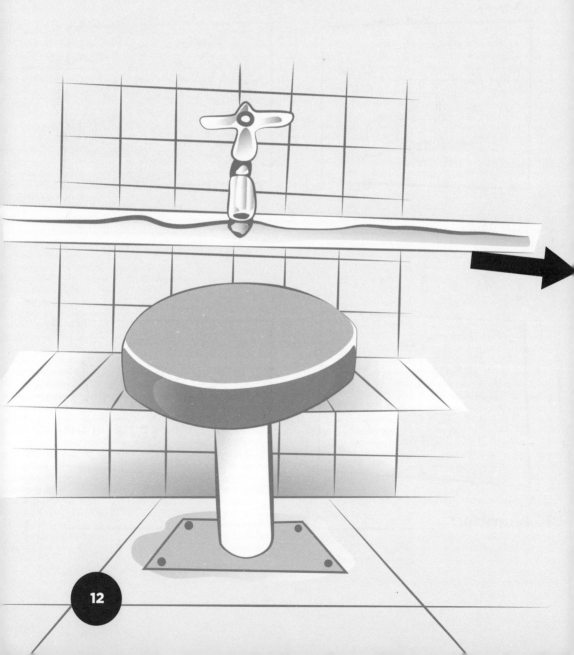

Sunan of Wuḍū'

Sunan of Wuḍū'

Using the box below, design and colour a poster with all the 13 sunan of wuḍū'. Remember to make the poster colourful.

Sunan of

— Always say bismillah

— Gargle 3 time

— Do maseh of head once

— wash both hand 3 times each

— Put water in nose 3 times

— Ithilal of the beard

— bresh your theeth with miswak

— make an intention

— wash each poorts in order

Wudu

— Do Khilou of fingers and toes.

— Wash each part befor the other part dries.

— Do Masah with both ears at once

— wash each part threetimes

Sunan of Wuḍū'

Put the actions of wuḍū' in order by writing a number on the line.

_2_ Always say Bismillāh

_4_ Gargle three times

_7_ Do masaḥ of the whole head once

_3_ Wash both hands three times each

_6_ Pass water into your nostrils three times

_9_ Khilāl of beard (pass wet hands in the beard)

_5_ Brush your teeth with a siwāk

_1_ Make an intention

_11_ Wash each part three times

_10_ Do khilāl of fingers and toes

_12_ Wash each part before the other part dries

_8_ Do masaḥ of both your ears once

_13_ Make sure to wash each part in order

Below is a list of different aspects of wuḍū'.

Your task is to find and colour in:

The Nawāqiḍ of wuḍū' in RED
The Makrūhāt of wuḍū' in YELLOW
The Mustaḥabbāt of wuḍū' in GREEN

VOMITING A MOUTHFUL Red

BEGIN WITH THE RIGHT HAND Yellow

FAINTING Red

CLEAN NOSE WITH RIGHT HAND Green

LAUGHING LOUDLY IN ṢALĀH Green

FACE THE QIBLAH yellow

FLOWING OF BLOOD FROM BODY Red

TALK ABOUT WORLDLY THINGS yellow

FALLING ASLEEP WHILST LEANING green

17

Tayammum

When can a person do tayammum?

Colour the bricks below and show your class how tayammum can be done with it.

Method of Ṣalāh

Number the pictures below to show the correct order of ṣalāh.

6

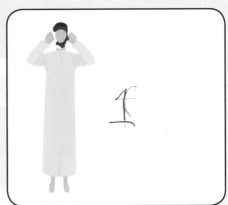

1

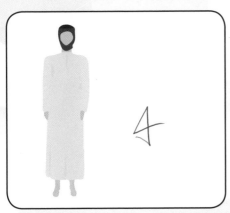

4

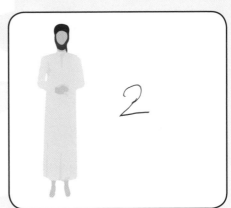

2

5

3

Aḥādīth

Truth

Translate the following ḥadīth, colour in the Arabic writing and then write down a few lessons you learnt from this ḥadīth.

_____

_____

_____

From this ḥadīth I learnt:

1._____

2._____

3._____

Salam

Translate the following ḥadīth, colour in the Arabic writing and then write down a few lessons you learnt from this ḥadīth.

إِنَّ أَوْلَى النَّاسِ بِاللهِ تَعَالَى مَنْ بَدَأَهُمْ بِالسَّلَامِ

_____

_____

_____

From this ḥadīth I learnt:

1. _____

2. _____

3. _____

Using the Right Hand

Translate the following ḥadīth, colour in the Arabic writing and then write down a few lessons you learnt from this ḥadīth.

سَمِّ اللَّهَ وَكُلْ بِيَمِيْنِكَ

_____

_____

_____

From this ḥadīth I learnt:

1._____

2._____

3._____

Drinking Whilst Sitting

Translate the following ḥadīth, colour in the Arabic writing and then write down a few lessons you learnt from this ḥadīth.

لَا يَشْرَبَنَّ أَحَدٌ مِنْكُمْ قَائِمًا

_____

_____

_____

From this ḥadīth I learnt:

1._____

2._____

3._____

24

Kindness to Neighbours

Translate the following ḥadīth, colour in the Arabic writing and then write down a few lessons you learnt from this ḥadīth.

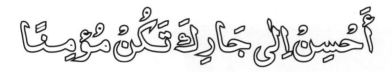

_____

_____

_____

From this ḥadīth I learnt:

1._____

2._____

3._____

Sīrah

سيرة النبي ﷺ

In the Cave of Ḥirā

1. Which cave did our Beloved Messenger Muḥammad ﷺ regularly visit?

_____

Draw a picture of a cave below and colour it in.

The First Revelation

2. Why did our Beloved Messenger Muḥammad ﷺ feel sad about the people of Makkah?

_____

3. What was the name of the angel who came with the revelation?

_____

4. What did the angel ask our Beloved Messenger Muḥammad ﷺ to do?

_____

The First Revelation

Find the **letters** from the lines below and then unscramble the word

29038i8639q9017

902r89153a97303

What is the word? _____

5. Who did Khadījah رضي الله عنها take our Beloved Messenger Muḥammad صلى الله عليه وسلم to?

_____

_____

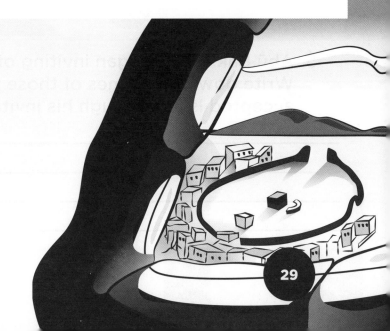

The First Believers

1. Who was the first woman to accept Islām?

_____

2. Who was Zayd ibn Ḥārithah رضي الله عنه?

_____

3. Who was 'Alī ibn Abī Ṭālib رضي الله عنه?

_____

4. Who was Abū Bakr رضي الله عنه?

_____

5. Abū Bakr رضي الله عنه began inviting others to Islām. Write down the names of those people who accepted Islām through his invitation.

_____

_____

_____

_____

The Invitation

1. Write down the translation of the āyah that Allāh ﷻ revealed to our Beloved Messenger Muḥammad ﷺ in which he commanded him to call his near relations to Islām.

   _____

2. Which clan did our Beloved Messenger Muḥammad ﷺ call for a meeting?

   _____

3. What did our Beloved Messenger Muḥammad ﷺ invite them all to?

   _____

4. Everyone listened except one person: who was he?

   _____

5. What did Abū Ṭālib say?

   _____

The Sermon on Mount Ṣafā

1. Which mountain did our Beloved Messenger Muḥammad ﷺ climb?

_____

_____

2. Which city is this mountain in?

_____

3. What did those people do who could not make it to the mountain?

_____

4. What did our Beloved Messenger Muḥammad ﷺ ask the Quraysh and what was their answer?

_____

_____

_____

_____

Trouble and Pain to the Early Muslims

1. Write down a few of the things that happened to Bilāl رضي الله عنه after accepting Islām.

   _____

   _____

2. What was Bilāl رضي الله عنه's answer when he was told to leave Islām?

   _____

3. Who was the first person to pass away in the path of Allāh سبحانه وتعالى?

   _____

4. Write down the names of other Ṣaḥābah who were hurt because of accepting Islām.

   _____

   _____

5. What did the Quraysh do to our Beloved Messenger Muḥammad صلى الله عليه وسلم one day whilst he was praying in the Masjid?

   _____

Tārīkh

تاريخ

Hūd

The people of 'Ād were given a lot by Allāh سبحانه وتعالى.
Draw and colour in some of the things that Allāh سبحانه وتعالى
has blessed us with.

Hūd عليه السلام

When the people of ʾĀd decided not to listen to Hūd عليه السلام, Allāh sent a punishment upon them.

Working with a partner, write down what happened to them when the punishment came and also write a lesson that you learn from their story.

The lesson that I learnt from their story is...

_____

_____

_____

Ṣāliḥ عليه السلام

1. Who were Thamūd?

2. Where did Thamūd live?

3. What did Thamūd worship?

4. Who was Ṣāliḥ عليه السلام?

5. What did he invite them to?

Ṣāliḥ عليه السلام

1. Did they listen to Ṣāliḥ عليه السلام ?

_____

2. What sign did they ask Ṣāliḥ عليه السلام for?

_____

3. Did Allāh سبحانه وتعالى send the sign they asked for?

_____

4. Did Thamūd believe after seeing the sign?

_____

5. What did they do to the sign that Allāh سبحانه وتعالى had sent to them?

_____

The Punishment

1. How many days did Thamūd have left before the punishment came?

_____

2. When they were told they only had some days left before the punishment, what did they do?

_____

3. How many people got together to go to Ṣāliḥ عليه السلام's house?

_____

4. What punishment came to them and what did it do to Thamūd?

_____

5. What lessons do we learn from the story of Ṣāliḥ عليه السلام?

_____
_____
_____
_____

Make your own word search using the words below and ask someone in your class to find the words.

'Ād

Thamūd

Ṣāliḥ

Hūd

Punishment

She Camel

ADD 2 MORE WORDS FROM THE STORIES OF HŪD عليه السلام **& ṢĀLIḤ** عليه السلام

1. _____

2. _____

'Aqā'id

Allāh the Protector

Write about a time when you were worried and how Allāh سبحانه وتعالى protected you.

MY STORY

Once I thagh I was going to fail my Test but th I made dua to pass my test and I did. So I was happy. And once when I was at the skate park I taught I was going to fall and get bruses but insted I did not fail and didn't get any bruses.

Allāh the All-Hearing

Write down the names of all the people you know from your family, relatives and friends.

Whilst writing these names, think and know that Allāh سبحانه وتعالى is listening to all these people and many more.

Allāh the All-Seeing

In this chapter you learnt of how Allāh سبحانه وتعالى can see us all the time.

Draw the pictures of the places where you think Muḥammad and Yūsuf hid and ate their sweets.

Allāh the One

Learn sūrah 112 and copy the translation from your Sūrah & Du'ā' book.

Sūrah 112

_____

_____

_____

_____

_____

Angels.

Fill in the blanks using the words below.

special	humans	exact	female
ordered	nūr (Light)	male	

Allāh سبحانه وتعالى made angels.

They are his _____ servants.

They are made of _____.

We cannot see them.

They are neither _____ nor _____.

They always obey Allāh سبحانه وتعالى. They do what He has _____ them to do. They never disobey Allāh سبحانه وتعالى.

They are not like _____.

They are countless and we don't know their _____ number, only Allāh سبحانه وتعالى knows.

Angels

Match the angel names to their main duties.

Jibra'īl	Questioners in the grave
Mikā'īl	Climate
Izrā'īl	Death
Isrāfīl	Trumpet
Kirāman Kātibīn	Recording deeds
Munkar Nakīr	Revelation

'Aqā'id

Angels

Learn and colour in the names of these angels.

Jibra'īl

Mikā'īl

Malakul Mawt

Isrāfīl

Kirāman Kātibīn

Munkar Nakīr

Books

Fill in the blanks using the words below.

waḥy	four	books	live
ṣuḥuf	Jibra'īl		

'Aqā'id

Allāh سبحانه وتعالى sent down many _____ to different prophets.

Allāh سبحانه وتعالى sent books to show us how to _____.

Allāh سبحانه وتعالى sent the books through the angel _____.

Revelation is called _____ in Arabic.

_____ books were sent down by Allāh سبحانه وتعالى.

Many other scrolls were sent with smaller messages. These were called _____.

Books

Below you will find the names of the four books that were revealed and the prophets they were sent down to. Your task is to colour the name of each book and the prophet it was sent to with the same colour. Use a different colour for each prophet.

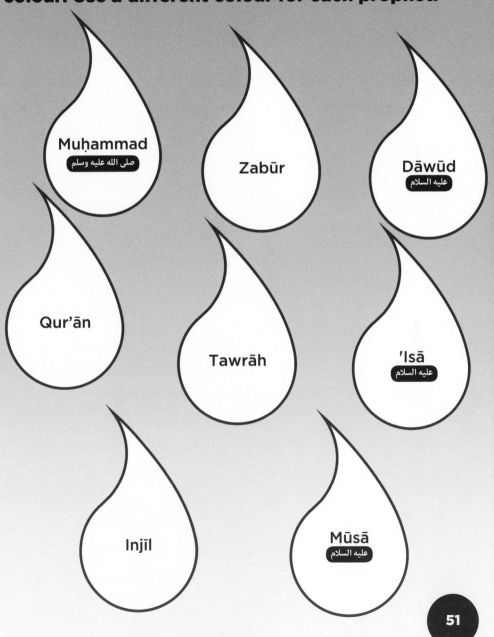

Muḥammad
صلى الله عليه وسلم

Zabūr

Dāwūd
عليه السلام

Qur'ān

Tawrāh

'Isā
عليه السلام

Injīl

Mūsā
عليه السلام

The Holy Qur'ān

Design and colour a poster about all the facts that you have learnt about the Qur'ān.

'Aqā'id

Keeping Promises

Colour these words in and remember them all the time.

KEEP YOUR PROMISE!

Keeping Promises

Copy out this ḥadīth in the box below and design a poster about it.

'Abdullāh Ibn Mas'ūd رضي الله عنه narrates that the Messenger of Allāh صلى الله عليه وسلم said: "The signs of the hypocrite are three: when he speaks he lies, when he makes a promise, he breaks it and when he is trusted he betrays the trust." (Ṣaḥīḥ al-Bukhārī)

Akhlāq

Keeping Promises

Write down three promises you have made or you want to make and write down the date next to them when you plan to fulfil these promises.

Promise 1   Date I will fulfil: _____

I promise to: _____
_____
_____
_____

Promise 2   Date I will fulfil: _____

I promise to: _____
_____
_____
_____

Promise 3   Date I will fulfil: _____

I promise to: _____
_____
_____
_____

Being Thankful

Allāh سبحانه وتعالى has bestowed many blessings upon us. Ask yourself: how would your life be without the blessings of Allāh سبحانه وتعالى?

Complete the table below and write down one or two words about how you would feel without these blessings of Allāh سبحانه وتعالى.

Blessings of Allāh	Life without the blessings of Allāh
Water	
Food	
Rain	
Sun	
Plants	
Animals	
Family	

Akhlāq

Being Thankful

Aqīlah learnt at madrasah that we should thank Allāh سبحانه وتعالى for everything we have. Help her think of things she can thank Allāh سبحانه وتعالى for.

Write or draw the things Allāh سبحانه وتعالى has given.

Being Thankful

Following the example below and remembering what you learnt in your coursebook, show how you can thank Allāh سبحانه وتعالى for the body parts mentioned.

Our Tongue

How can we thank Allāh سبحانه وتعالى for this great gift?

Firstly we say الْحَمْدُ لِلّٰه Alḥamdulillāh.

Secondly we should be happy that we have a tongue to speak with.

Finally, we should make sure we do not use the tongue in saying those things which displease Allāh سبحانه وتعالى.

Our hands

1. _____
2. _____
3. _____

Our eyes

1. _____
2. _____
3. _____

Our ears

1. _____
2. _____
3. _____

THANK YOU!
Jazākallāhu
Khayrā

Being Thankful

In the box below, colour the logs in and draw some fire around them to show what happens to our good deeds when we do not thank Allāh سبحانه وتعالى for what we have and we become jealous of others.

Our Beloved Messenger Muḥammad صلى الله عليه وسلم told us "Jealousy eats up good actions, just like fire eats up wood." (Abū Dāwūd)

Being Thankful

Always remember to say 'Jazākallāhu Khayrā' when someone gives us something.

Colour in the Arabic and English words for 'Jazākallāhu Khayrā'

Spreading Salām

Spread salām in these speech bubbles by colouring in the words of salām in each one. Try writing your own in the last one

Spreading Salām

Think, draw and colour all the places you might meet people so you can say salām to them.

One has been done for you.

Spreading Salām

Colour and remember this important line:

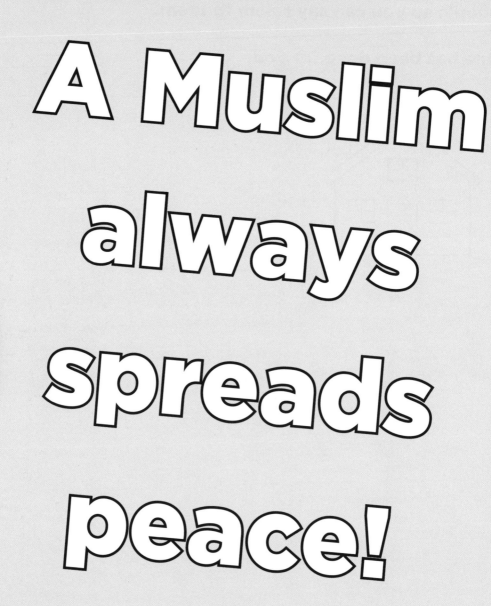

A Muslim always spreads peace!

Helping in Good Things

Help Fāṭimah as she takes a milk carton home for her mother.

Helping in Good Things

Zakariyyā and Muṣṭafā want to help the poor people in different countries by giving them water.

Count how many water bottles they are sending to each country.

Country 1   **Amount:** _____

Country 2   **Amount:** _____

Country 3   **Amount:** _____

How many bottles are there in total? _____

If you sent 5 bottles to Zambia, 8 to Rwanda and 15 to Malawi, how many bottles did you send all together? _____

Helping in Good Things

Māriyah and Zakiyyah are helping to clean up at home. Help them by drawing arrows and send each object to the correct place.

Kindness to Animals

Write down ten animal names that you know and for each one write down one way we can be kind to them.

Animal name	How we can be kind to them
Example: Camels	Not to put so much luggage on their backs.
1. _____	_____
2. _____	_____
3. _____	_____
4. _____	_____
5. _____	_____
6. _____	_____
7. _____	_____
8. _____	_____
9. _____	_____
10. _____	_____

Kindness to Animals

Name four animals and describe them below using three words each.

Example: Lion - Strong, fierce and scary

1. _____   _____

2. _____   _____

3. _____   _____

4. _____   _____

Ādāb

Ādāb of Salām

**Write down one adab of salām next to each letter.
Don't forget to colour the letter in.**

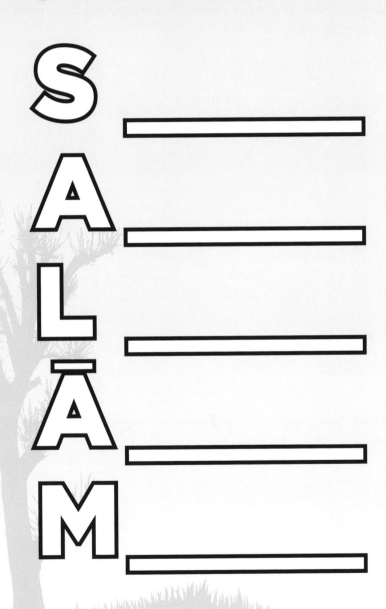

Ādāb of Salām

Write down how much reward a person can get for saying the following:

Ādāb of Salām

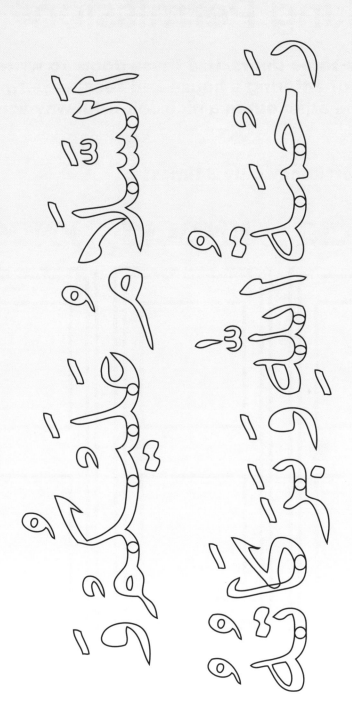

Entering a House and Seeking Permission

Below are three doors. Use these doors to write down the ādāb of entering a house and seeking permission. Spread the ādāb out in a nice colourful way across the doors.

Remember: knock only 3 times!

Entering a House and Seeking Permission

You have a friend in another country and you want to share what you have learnt this year.

Design a postcard letting the friend know how you are and what you have learnt about the ādāb of entering the house and seeking permission.

Ādāb

Entering a House and Seeking Permission

Draw and colour a picture of a house and think about how you would ask permission when entering.

Ādāb of Speaking

Work with a partner discuss the ādāb of speaking and write them all in these speech bubbles.

Ādāb of Sneezing and Yawning

Write the ādāb of sneezing around the tissue box.

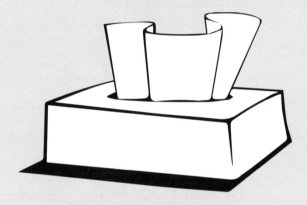

Write the ādāb of yawning around the hand.

82